C
Littl

Charles M. Schulz

RR
RAVETTE PUBLISHING

First published in 2001 by
Ravette Publishing Limited, Unit 3, Tristar Centre,
Star Road, Partridge Green, West Sussex RH13 8RA

Edited by Gordon Volke

Printed in Malta by Gutenberg Press

ISBN: 1 84161 099 2

Charlie Brown is the world's famous 'blockhead'. He is the average, mediocre, unpopular, self-doubting innocent character that everyone identifies with, making him a sort of Everyman.

Although Charlie Brown is friendly and polite, he is a worrier who frets over his unrequited loves from the little red-haired girl to his own dog, Snoopy.

There are certain aspects of Charlie Brown's life that will never change ... Lucy will never let him kick the football, he'll never succeed in flying his kite and except for one famous occasion (when the baseball pitcher was a little girl who was in love with him) he'll never hit a home run.

If only Charlie Brown knew how much the world loves him, he might not be so full of grief ... but then he wouldn't be Charlie Brown!

Life is easier if you only
dread one day at a time.

When we lose, I'm miserable ...
When we win, I feel guilty!

When you have to get up at 7.00,
6.59 is the worst time of day!

Summers always fly ...
winters walk!

Life is full of choices,
but you never get any!

Registration
NOTICE
ALL CLASSES
IN ART, SHOP
AND FRISBEE
ARE FILLED

I fall in love with any girl
who smells like library paste!

"It's better to give than receive"
is certainly true of advice!

PSYCHIATRIC
HELP 5¢
THE DOCTOR
IS IN

Lovers don't send
junk mail.

As they say, it's not who wins that counts, it's how you play the game – but why do we have to play so lousy?

Sometimes I think life and I are going in different directions!

"It's a shame that it has to snow only in the winter ... if it snowed in the summer, a person could stay outside longer, and enjoy it more!"

It's no fun playing
hide-and-seek when no-one
comes to look for you!

Don't worry about the world
coming to an end today.
It's already tomorrow
in Australia.

Every time there's a good suggestion, someone brings up the budget!

If light travels so fast,
how come the afternoons
are so long?

Life is like an ice cream cone:
You have to learn to lick it!

Nothing is ever as much fun
as you thought it was
going to be.

I’ve developed a new philosophy – I only dread one day at a time.

Everything I learn,
I learn the *Hard* way ...
in school!

Candy bars are like years.
We're paying more,
but they're getting shorter.

There's an old legend
that says if you stand in front
of your mailbox long enough,
you'll receive a Valentine.

It's kind of nice to bring happiness into someone's life.

Learn from yesterday ... live for today ... look to tomorrow ... rest this afternoon!

It's hard to tell everybody
they can go home
if nobody shows up.

No problem is so big or complicated that it can't be run away from!

I hate these practice sessions!

Small trophies are
for hollow victories.

I learned a lot at the art museum – I'll never be Andrew Wyeth!

I'm self educated – everything
I've learned, I've learned
watching TV!

The way the population is rising, I'm getting more unpopular every day!

If you're not sure she loves you,
blockhead her out of your mind.

The only time nobody
laughs at me is when
I'm *Trying* to be funny!

I'm the only person I know
who had to go out and
buy himself a Christmas card.

I didn't think being right mattered, as long as I was sincere!

Life can be as full as a grocery trolley ... unless you have six items or less.

My dog was the only one in
our class to get a perfect
score in the true-or-false test!

School time doesn't 'roll around'
... it leaps right out at you!

If life is like a baseball game,
try to find out how many
innings they're playing.

HOME
VISITORS

I'm at my best in something
where the answers are
mostly a matter of opinion.

Nothing echoes
like an empty mailbox.

In the game of life,
I’m always hitting
from the back tees!

As soon as I get up
in the morning,
I feel like I'm in over my head.

When you're depressed,
it helps to lean your head on
your arm and stare into space –
if you're unusually depressed,
you may have to change arms.

Never lie in bed at night
asking yourself questions
you can't answer ...

Life is full of choices,
but you never get any!